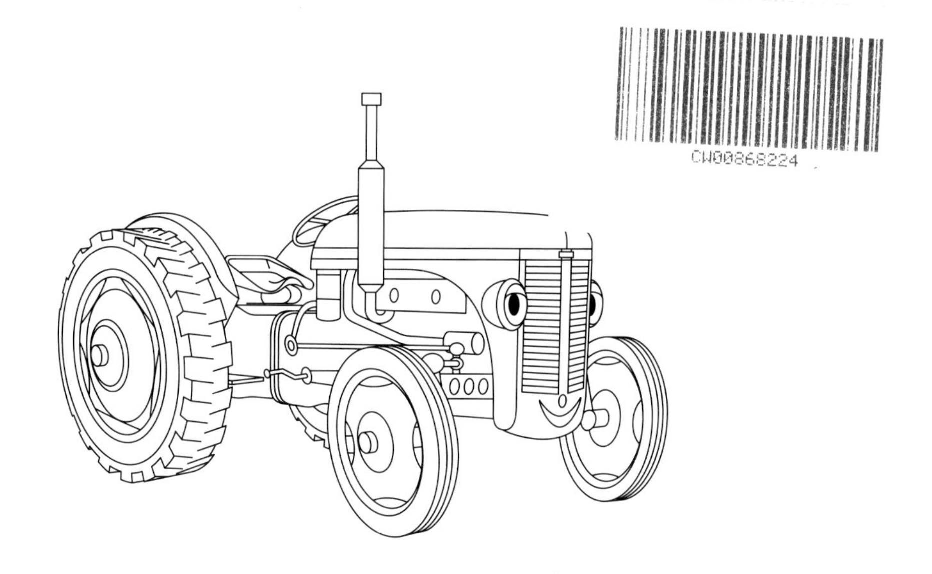

FERGUS AND THE HEATWAVE

Fergus the little grey tractor and his friend Berty the Thirty were outside their barn, on the farm where they live with Farmer Pete.

The sun was shining and it was very hot.

"It is so hot I think the paint on my bonnet might peel off," said Fergus to Berty.

"I have never known it to be this hot before," said Berty.

It had been a very hot summer with no rain for several weeks.
The ground was hard and the grass fields were turning golden yellow.

"Farmer Pete will have to do something soon," said Fergus.
"The cows will be getting hot and uncomfortable."

"Farmer Pete always says that happy cows give the best milk," replied Berty. "He will have to cool them down somehow."

Later on Farmer Pete and Young Timmy came over to the farmyard.

Farmer Pete started Fergus and drove him into the barn where the attachments are kept.

Fergus felt much better in the cool barn.

“I have a job you will really enjoy,” said Farmer Pete.

With the help of Young Timmy he attached a water pump to Fergus.

When the pump was secure, they placed some large water hoses on top.

"I would like you to pick up the water tanker with Berty the Thirty," Farmer Pete said to Young Timmy, "and when you've finished follow me to the pond."

Fergus, Farmer Pete, Berty and Young Timmy set off across the fields and soon arrived at the pond.

7

The pond is filled by a fresh water spring and Farmer Pete knows there is always plenty of water for him to use.

At the pond they attached the hoses to Fergus' pump. One hose they placed in the pond, the other they connected to the top of the water tanker.

Farmer Pete started the pump and Fergus began pumping the water into Berty's tanker.

F
E
7

Soon the tanker was full of fresh cool water from the pond.

Farmer Pete rolled up the hoses and set off on Fergus with Young Timmy on Berty the Thirty following behind.

Farmer Pete drove Fergus across the fields to the woods where the cows were lying in the shade of the trees.

None of the cows moved when they arrived,
they were all too hot.

74
14
15
9
21

Farmer Pete stopped Fergus and unrolled the hoses again.

This time he connected one hose to the tanker, whilst on the other hose he attached a spray nozzle.

Once again Farmer Pete started the pump on the back of Fergus. Young Timmy pointed the spray nozzle in the air.

7

The water started to spray from the end of the nozzle, all over the hot cows. The cows liked this so much they licked their noses and twitched their ears.

The water began to soak and cool the cows, the spray was also falling on Farmer Pete, Young Timmy, Fergus and Berty.

"This is nice," said Fergus to Berty. "My paintwork is cooler already, with a bit of luck we might have
to do this every day."

3
7

Farmer Pete and Young Timmy took it in turns to spray the cool water onto the cows and tractors, until the tank began to make gurgling, empty noises.

"That should help to keep them happy until milking time," said Young Timmy.

Farmer Pete stopped the pump and then rolled the hoses back up again. They then drove the tractors back to the farmyard.

7
74
15

At the farmyard Young Timmy put the water tanker back in it's place, while Farmer Pete put Fergus back in the shade of the barn.

When Berty was back alongside Fergus, Farmer Pete said, "we will leave the pump on the back of Fergus, as we will have to do this every day while it's so hot."

Farmer Pete knew it was the best way to help keep the cows cool and happy.

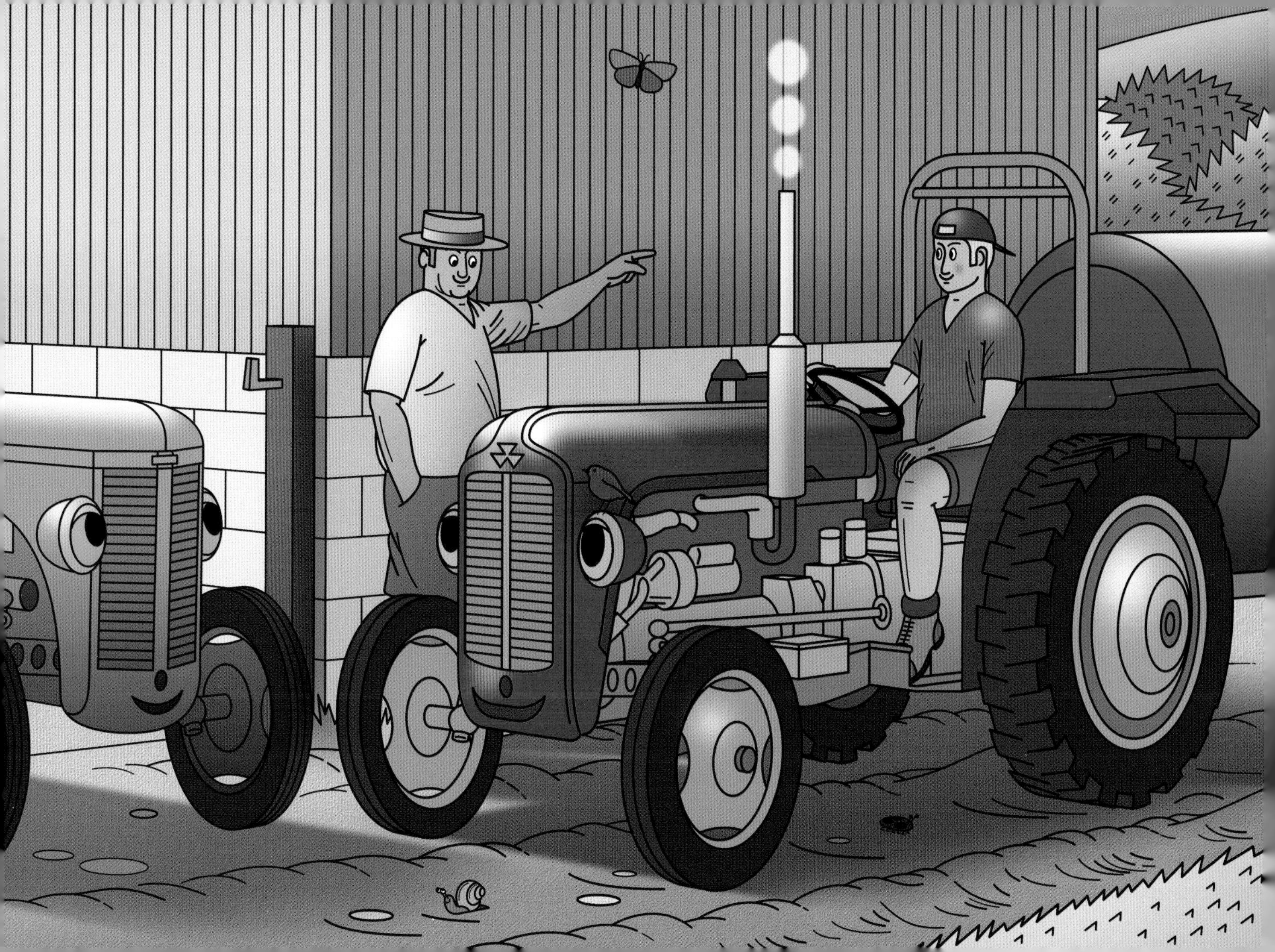

"That is really good news," Fergus said to Berty. "I really enjoyed that cool shower."

"The cows liked it as well," Berty replied.

"I think the cows liked it as much as we did," said Fergus.

That afternoon they rested in the shade of the barn, waiting for the evening to come. When they could tell stories to each other and fall asleep dreaming of their cool shower tomorrow.

FERGUS' STORY MR COOMBS THE GAMEKEEPER GEOF
THE MECHANIC FERGUS GETS A NEW FRIEND NEVILL
GETS HIS NAME NEVILLE AND THE HOT AIR BALLOO
FERGUS' BONFIRE NIGHT FERGUS AT THE BARN FIR
FERGUS AND BERTY CLEAR THE SNOW FERGUS' CHRISTMA
SPECIAL THE SPRING TIME SURPRISE FERGUS AND TH
NEW BUILDING FERGUS' HALLOWEEN FERGUS AND TH
STEAM UP FERGUS AND BERTY GO POTATO PLANTIN
FERGUS AND THE BEAVER SCOUTS THE WEDDING DA
FERGUS AND THE FLOOD FERGUS AT THE CIRCUS FERGU
AND THE HEATWAVE FERGUS AT THE CARNIVAL FERGU
AT THE PLOUGHING MATCH FERGUS AND THE FALLEN TRE
FERGUS' STORY MR COOMBS THE GAMEKEEPER GEOF
THE MECHANIC FERGUS GETS A NEW FRIEND NEVILL
GETS HIS NAME NEVILLE AND THE HOT AIR BALLOO
FERGUS' BONFIRE NIGHT FERGUS AT THE BARN FIR
FERGUS AND BERTY CLEAR THE SNOW FERGUS' CHRISTMA